Illustrations by Jimmy Glen

Can YOU find Wullie in the places listed below?

- BURNS SUPPER, BURNS COTTAGE, ALLOWAY
- KELVINGROVE ART GALLERY AND MUSEUM, GLASGOW
- FOOTBALL AT STARKS PARK, KIRKCALDY
- LOCH NESS FESTIVAL
- STIRLING CASTLE
- WOW IN THE PARK
- THE OPEN CHAMPIONSHIP, ST ANDREWS
- OBAN, THE GATEWAY TO THE ISLES

- THE ROYAL EDINBURGH MILITARY TATTOO
- LARGS VIKING FESTIVAL
- THE BRAEMAR GATHERING
- RIVERSIDE MUSEUM, GLASGOW
- THE FALKIRK WHEEL
- COMICS CONVENTION, DUNDEE
- HOGMANAY, PRINCES STREET, EDINBURGH
- THE COMMONWEALTH GAMES, GLASGOW

OOR WULLIE! YOUR WULLIE! A'BODY'S WULLIE!

Oor Wullie is immediately recognisable with his spiky hair, dungarees and tackety boots, and he's often found sitting on his upturned bucket.

Many of his adventures start off as pocket money-making schemes that sometimes don't turn out as planned, exasperating his parents (Ma and Pa) and Primrose Patterson (Wullie's sometime girlfriend) and frequently involving the local policeman PC Murdoch.

Oor Wullie's best pals are Fat Bob, Wee Eck and Soapy Soutar. The gang often meets in Wullie's shed which is where many adventures are discussed, plans are laid and inventions are constructed.

Oor Wullie has another best pal – a dog – Harry the Westie, and he has a pet mouse (Jeemy), a rabbit called Jockie, a goldfish named Joey and is fascinated by worms, tadpoles and he even has a pet frog.

Oor Wullie's favourite things tae dae are:

bein' oot an' aboot, playin' fitba' (football), makin' models, cyclin', campin' oot, writin' pomes (poems), fishin', playin' the moothie (mouth organ), buildin' an' ridin' carties, sledgin' in the snaw (snow), flyin' kites an' gliders, doin' magic tricks, playin' wi' magnets and firin' catties (catapults) an' pea shooters.

Oor Wullie's favourite things tae eat are:

porridge, bacon & eggs, Scotch Broth, mince & tatties (potatoes) & peas, jeely pieces (jam sandwiches), fish & chips, semolina puddin', ice cream, Soor Plooms (acidic boiled sweets).

Oor Wullie's favourite things tae drink are:

skoosh (fizzy drink), sasparrilla and sugarelly (made with liquorice and water, it's more fun to make than drink!).

PC Murdoch

Me

Primrose

Ma

Pa

Fat Bob

Soapy Soutar

Harry

Wee Eck

Jeemy

Whaur's (Where's) Oor Wullie?

You can see what Oor Wullie (and his bucket), Fat Bob, Soapy Soutar, Wee Eck, PC Murdoch and Jeemy the moose all look like in the group picture above.

These are the other objects you will be looking for:

String of sausages

Wee dog

Speug (sparrow)

Mouse

Football

Stuffed fish

Wally dug (china dog)

Ice cream cone

Haggis

Pea shooter

Medal

• BURNS SUPPER, BURNS COTTAGE, ALLOWAY

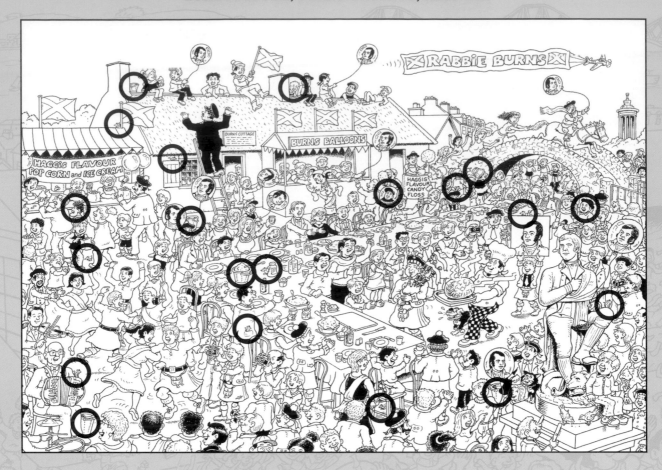

• KELVINGROVE ART GALLERY AND MUSEUM, GLASGOW

• FOOTBALL AT STARKS PARK, KIRKCALDY

• LOCH NESS FESTIVAL

• THE OPEN CHAMPIONSHIP, ST ANDREWS

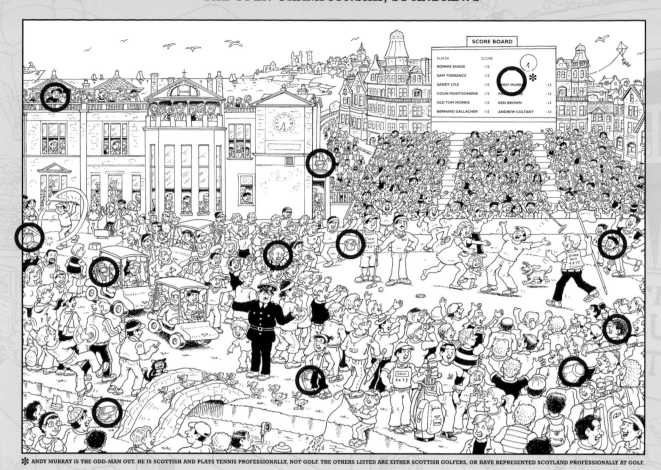

SCORE BOARD

PLAYER	SCORE		
RONNIE SHADE	-12		
SAM TORRANCE	-12	ANDY MURRAY	*
SANDY LYLE	-12		-12
COLIN MONTGOMERIE	-12		-12
OLD TOM MORRIS	-12	KEN BROWN	-12
BERNARD GALLACHER	-12	ANDREW COLTART	-12

✳ ANDY MURRAY IS THE ODD-MAN OUT. HE IS SCOTTISH AND PLAYS TENNIS PROFESSIONALLY, NOT GOLF. THE OTHERS LISTED ARE EITHER SCOTTISH GOLFERS, OR HAVE REPRESENTED SCOTLAND PROFESSIONALLY AT GOLF.

• OBAN, THE GATEWAY TO THE ISLES

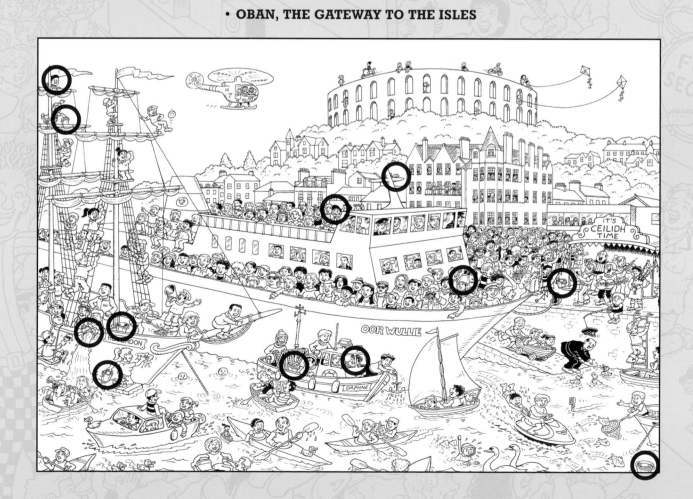

• THE BRAEMAR GATHERING

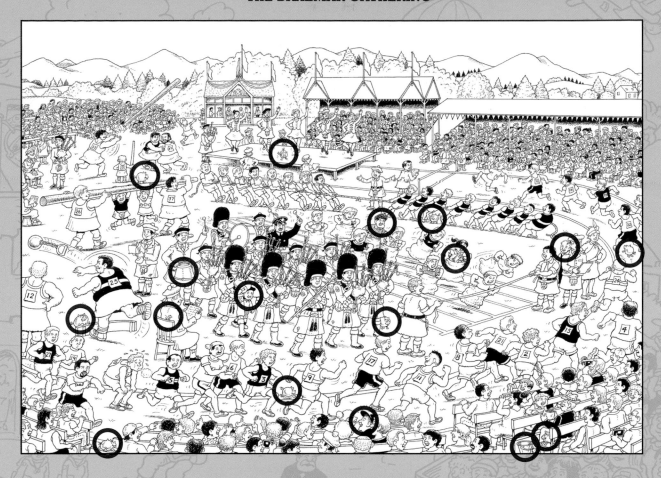

• RIVERSIDE MUSEUM, GLASGOW

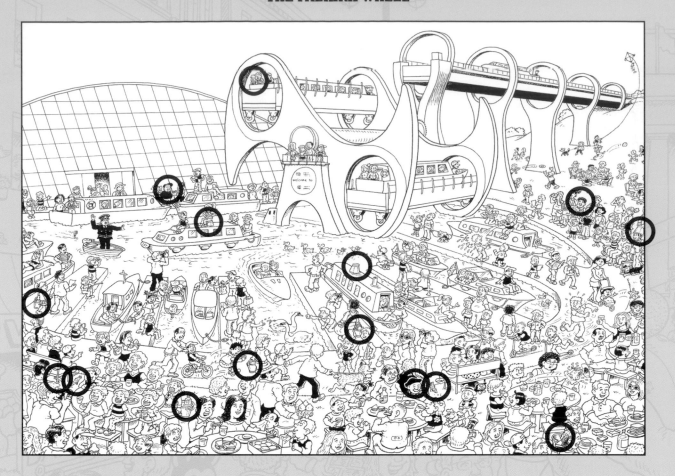

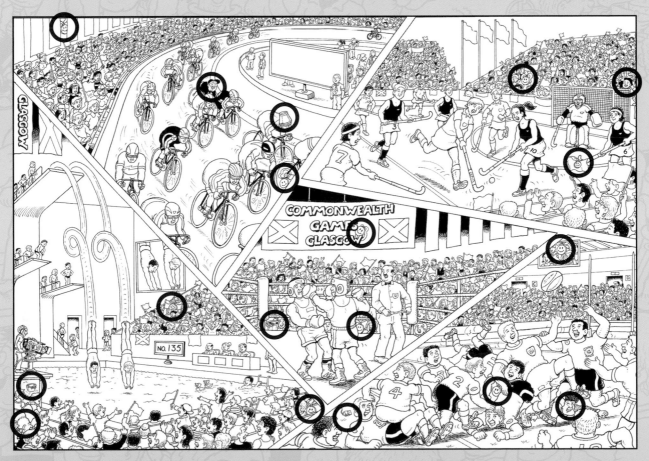

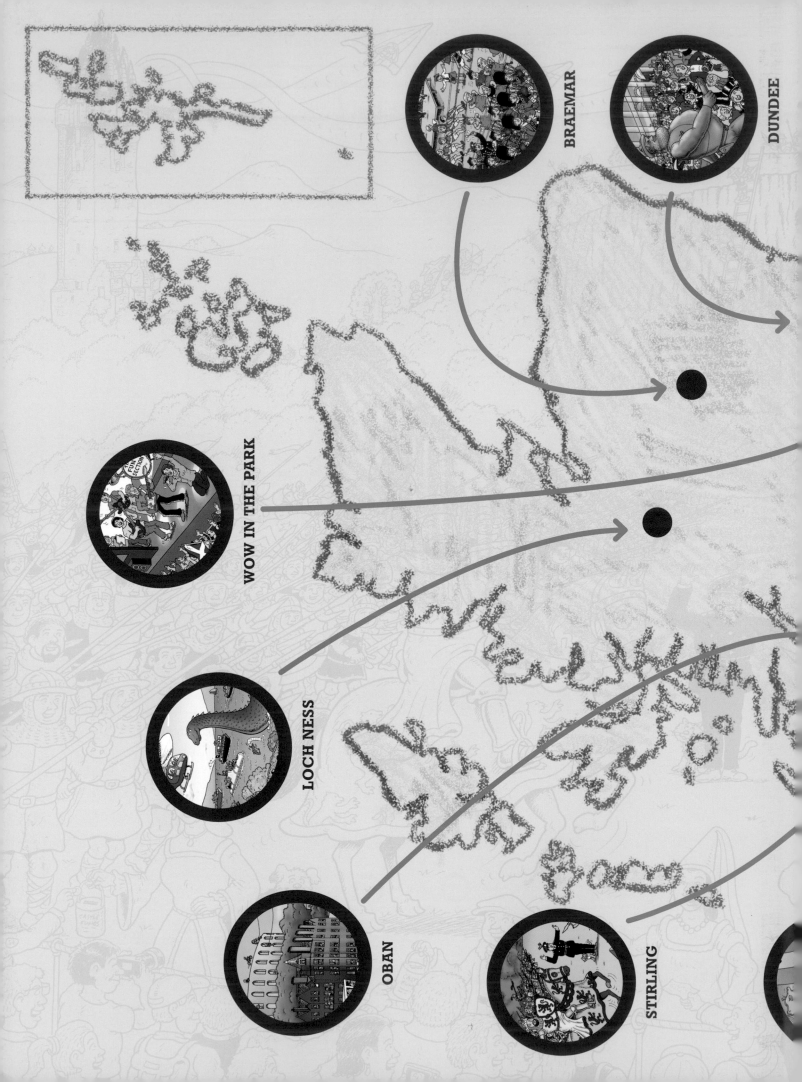

BRAEMAR

DUNDEE

WOW IN THE PARK

LOCH NESS

OBAN

STIRLING